# Alison

# Also by Lizzy Stewart

For adults

*Walking Distance*
*It's Not What You Thought It Would Be*

For children

*There's a Tiger in the Garden*
*Juniper Jupiter*
*The Way to Treasure Island*

# Alison

## Lizzy Stewart

First published in Great Britain in 2022 by
Serpent's Tail,
an imprint of Profile Books Ltd
29 Cloth Fair
London
EC1A 7JQ
*www.serpentstail.com*

Text copyright © Lizzy Stewart, 2022
Illustrations copyright © Lizzy Stewart, 2022

Consultant: Ayoola Solarin

3 5 7 9 10 8 6 4 2

Printed and bound in Italy by L.E.G.O. Spa

A CIP catalogue record for this book is available from the British Library.

ISBN 978 1 78816 905 9
eISBN 978 1 78283 898 2

For Mum, Becky and Jess.

With Love.

**M**y name is Alison Porter and I began my life, in 1958, in Bridport, Dorset. My parents had grown up in Dorset, and their parents before them. My dad worked in the local bank and my mum did repairs and alterations for a nearby dressmaker. My brother, Michael, was four years older than me. We were almost friends growing up. Almost, but not quite.

I think we were happy. We were certainly ordinary, which made us assume that we must be happy. Whether we felt it or not.

Andrew was twenty when I met him and I was seventeen. Andrew. I would say his name under my breath before I went to sleep. His name was the incantation that summoned the rush of intense feelings I so desperately craved. I don't doubt that it was love, but it was love for Andrew mixed in with love of love. In the early stages it was also a feverish obsession. It was madness. I'd wait in the park till my hands turned grey-blue so that I could catch him on his way home from work. I'd pretend to be absorbed in my reading and would look up nonchalantly as he passed. I saved up my pocket money (rarely doled out and meagre when it was) to buy the records he talked about. I pushed my own records under the bed, I took down my posters, incriminating evidence that I had once been a thirteen-year-old girl. I changed for him, though he never once asked me to.

I left school four months after we met, knowing that we would, surely, get married within the year. It wasn't a smart decision but no one tried to talk me out of it. My parents adored him. He was nice. I was fast-tracking my route to an ordinary life. It made sense; an ordinary life seemed like the right thing to do.

Three days after I turned eighteen, with a paper-hatted birthday party in the back garden, we got married, quietly, in a registry office. My mum was furious that we didn't get married in the church but I didn't care. We felt so modern.

3

We felt modern but we weren't, not really, and we barely knew each other. We were just kids from the coast who had opted for the most straightforward course of action. There hadn't been a point where we'd stopped to consider what the alternative might be.

We were poor. Not tragically so, but enough that every day was built around working out how to stretch Andrew's paltry pay-cheque across the whole month. He worked for the town council, in an administrative role that I could not muster the interest to ask about. I took on sewing and mending work for the local girls' school. Which made me feel like a good Victorian wife, and, more worryingly, a lot like my mother.

Our house was 15 miles from the town we both grew up in. It felt like making a fresh start but it wasn't. We'd rented it from the big estate that owned most of the houses along the cliffs. They'd painted them all the same shade of pale yellow to try and create a sense of local, historical spirit. I thought, really, the yellow paint was an attempt to hide the weather-beaten dilapidation that befell most of the buildings in the area.

Inside it was dark and chilly, and I was on my own a lot of the time. The bath was in a poorly constructed extension that rattled in high winds. Even in summer I struggled to find a spot where the light was strong enough to sew a cushion cover or read a book, and often ended up dragging half the living room outdoors to do my work.

Nevertheless, we tried our hardest to be happy.

But I was bored and I was lonely.

The thing about our marriage was that there was no one thing about it. No one thing that told me why I was there, nor why I would ever leave.

Two years in I realised that my life was no better or worse because of it. I think every girl wants better or worse, ideally better, I suppose. But sometimes worse can be so delicious, so enlivening that we'll take it, simply to have something to do.

Andrew could tell that I was struggling, but he couldn't figure out why. He was a good, kind man but he was only a few years older than me, and he had even less of an idea of who I was than I did. He suggested that I find a hobby, something to fill my days. I didn't tell him that my days were full already. I didn't want him to know that it took all the energy I had just to keep our terrible little house running. Instead I went, obediently, to the library to research potential outlets for my aimlessness.

Gosh. How very dull.

Well, do you have a hobby, then?

Of course not. Hobbies are only necessary if your life isn't interesting. And mine is.

Lucky you.

And yours isn't? Wafting your lovely way through libraries, catching the eye of every man here. Calling life to you like a siren.

I don't think that's what happened.

That's exactly what happened, as far as I see it.

Agree to disagree.

I need to get home. Nice to, um, meet you.

Patrick.

Nice to meet you, Patrick.

And your name?

Um. Alison. Alison Porter.

Well, Alison Porter. It was lovely, in the truest sense.

And if you still need a hobby on Tuesday, I'm running a little art class at the William Lang. An evening thing. You'll have to phone them for details as I don't remember the specifics. You'd be welcome.

**I** didn't know what the William Lang was. I sat in the hallway that evening with the phone book on my knees, frantically turning the pages.

'What's the William Lang?'

'Shouldn't that be who?'

'Oh. I don't know.'

'Sounds like a man's name.'

'Yes. But … I think it must be a place.'

'A place? Called William? Bit strange. Oh, wait, is it the gallery? That funny little place past the accountant's office?'

'Is it? Ahh. That makes sense. I think that's it.'

'Why d'you want to know?'

'There's a class there, I think. An art class. I thought I could go for … you know … a hobby?'

'Sounds like a good plan, love. A bit of watercolour and a few cups of tea. Sounds perfect.'

'Yeah … Yeah.'

13

**P**atrick didn't live in Dorset; he lived in London. His full name was Patrick Kerr and he was a well-known and well-respected painter, a member of the Royal Academy. He was spending a month and a half in Dorset sitting the house of his friend Roger Blake-Kelly, another painter. I hadn't heard of either of them. They called him 'the last great painter'. He would roll his eyes whenever the phrase came up. 'The last ailing dinosaur in a world filled with shiny new humans,' he'd laugh.

**H**e was born in Oxfordshire in 1931, to wealthy, educated parents who supported his painting from an early age. He studied at the Slade and then the Royal College of Art in the fifties, encouraged by tutors who doubled up as pioneers of British Pop Art and abstraction. He began as a jobbing portrait painter but quickly became accepted by the art world owing, mainly, to his talent but also to a convenient mix of good looks, good breeding and innate ability to charm. His ascent was rapid. Six years after graduating from the Royal College his work could be seen in galleries across London and then in Paris. After ten years he had sold paintings to the Tate and the National Portrait Gallery. His story was everyone else's dream. He was talented and he was celebrated and rewarded for that talent after only a few short years of trying.

He valued paint above all things. It wasn't that he disliked the new trends in video art and performance but that they didn't register with him at all. They weren't art in the way that he knew it. Paint, though – paint was noble and honest and the 'realm of true genius'.

His friends were all glamorous and accomplished; writers, photographers and people who 'owned things', galleries, theatres, publishing houses … Most of them were men. A fact that I don't think ever crossed his mind. For a long time I didn't see him as part of the problem, though he certainly was to some extent. He was fiercely anti-establishment in the way that only someone so deeply adored by the establishment *could* be. They gifted him the money and, thus, the freedom to devote his life to painting. He had no time for people who didn't live exactly as they chose, as he did; he couldn't fathom why you'd adhere to convention. He didn't know that most people have to; that space to move only exists around a select few.

I thought I needed Dorset. The air, the saltwater and so on, but my God if I can't wait to get back to London now. Not least for a decent glass of wine.

Don't look so wounded! I'm not going to leave for another week. Roger would be totally livid if I left the garden unattended for even a day.

And I've not grown tired of you either. You fascinate me, Alison, with your big eyes and that wretched jumper.

Anyway! Why don't you show me what you did in the class today?

These are good! A little heavy-handed ... here and ... here. You need better paper. You can't work on this shit. I'll get you some when I'm in London.

The real students are so much better than me, I think. You can tell that they're ... artists. You know?

18

You can tell they're artists because they've spent ages curating their wardrobes and the books they leave carefully scattered across the table, not because of how they draw. You're raw and unfussy. Truthful, even. I think you could be very good one day. With work.

Do you think?

With hard work, yes. And some teaching.

I won't have a teacher after you leave.

I can still teach you. You'll have to come to London. You won't learn much around here.

I ... I can't.

Well, it's up to you. In the meantime, I'd like you to come sit for me this weekend. I want to paint you.

Paint me?

Yes.

Me?

Don't look so scared. You can keep your clothes on!

Oh ... Can I?

19

**S**itting is an art. Some people can do it, some people can't. I was a good sitter. I was still and quiet. That first day I kept my clothes on, as he'd assured me I could. It wasn't long though – days or weeks, I don't remember – before I removed them for him. Initially, when I sat for Patrick I felt so self-conscious. I'd try to hide the parts of myself I didn't like. I'd hold in my little stomach, angle my arms so that they weren't flattened wide against my sides. I'd end the day totally exhausted, my muscles aching from hours of self-conscious tensing. After a while I stopped. Patrick didn't say anything; he probably didn't notice the difference, if there even was one. I suppose you can't really hide yourself with no clothes on.

I always knew where he was looking, which part of me he was painting, because his eyes seemed to draw a physical line across my body. It was a powerful feeling. I think I was probably giddy on that feeling, that totally unbroken attention, for a very long time. Longer than I should have been.

Later, when I had sitters of my own, I encouraged them to enjoy the silence. To do nothing at all. Some would be uncomfortable and we'd have to put the radio on but most people appreciated it. What a thing to be quiet and still in your own body. No demands on you but the requirement that you simply be there for me to look at. My favourite sitter was a woman called Sofie who would cry as she sat for me. I asked what was making her sad and she said, in lilting Norwegian-inflected English, 'It's not sadness crying. It's cathartic, to sit for you and to be naked and valued, and celebrated, I suppose. I cry because … I may as well. It feels like a good time to get it out.'

21

23

**W**hat do you do with an offer like that, when you're twenty years old and have never really known the world or what you wanted?

You let thoughts of him consume you.

You do not consider the specifics of your feelings for him, only his for you; how they outweigh everything in your own small life, how they come from this great man, who is so much bigger than you. It must mean something. It must make you special.

What do you do when someone with so much seems to offer it all to you, who has so little? You let it overpower you. You think of him all day, for three full days, before you find yourself at his door.

I loved Patrick Kerr as a trapdoor out of my life long before I found I could love him as a man.

**I** left Andrew; of course I did.

The leaving was slow, drawn out. On television people just walk out. In real life there was long conversation after long conversation. In some of those many conversations I cried, and in others he cried. Sometimes we both cried, just sobbed and sobbed helplessly at each other before climbing silently into bed where we failed to sleep, each so conscious of the other and the endless whirl of feeling in the gap between us.

Patrick returned to London just one month after our first encounter in the library but it was another three long, sad months until I caught up with him.

I've found you a great little place near Euston.

What?

Near Euston. A flat. It's small but the windows are good. Good windows are important.

I mean... I thought... I...

What did you think?

...Nothing.

Alison... what did you think?

I thought I'd live... where you live?

Oh, my darling! NO! No, no, no. I have to work!

I know... I know that. I... I just thought...

Darling girl, Are you sad? Have I upset you?

No, no. Of course not.

The thing is, lovely girl, I am quite unbearable. A total nightmare. I wake at all hours, I storm about. I can't cook and I refuse to learn. The whole place smells like turpentine all the time. There are sitters coming in and out of the house all day. It would be the absolute worst place to make you live. You'd hate me within days. And we don't want that. I don't want that. I couldn't stand that.

Me neither. I mean, I'm sure I wouldn't hate you, but...

This way we spend time together at your flat and do our work at mine. It's only a short walk between the two but I think it's vital we keep the two worlds separate. Church and State.

It was a small flat above a long-closed-up newsagent. I shared a bathroom with the couple who lived upstairs. I never saw them but I found their clippings and cuttings in the gaps between floor tiles and stuck to the inside of the sink. I had a bedroom and a second room that functioned as a kitchen, a living room, a dining room and a workspace. I didn't have a television – I don't think Patrick would have approved of a television. I did have a radio, which was on all the time, and a small bookcase that held whatever Patrick was suggesting I read. I read everything he gave me.

Each morning I went to Regent's Park and walked a giant circle around the whole thing. That felt, I was sure, like enough exercise to keep me healthy. After that I'd return home and read for half an hour before making myself a snack of tomatoes and cheese, then I'd walk to Patrick's.

I'd sit for Patrick for anywhere between two and eight hours. Once I sat for thirteen hours and passed out when I tried to stand up. He'd paint me and I'd listen to him explain how he was mixing his colours, or how he was using linseed oil to slow the drying time of the paint. I sat and sat and sat.

The sitting was, almost always, followed by sex, often on the pile of fusty mattresses and pillows he'd arranged for me to pose on. All that looking followed by touch was a thrill; I couldn't believe how exciting it was. I was young and I imagined that Patrick was torturing himself by not touching me whilst he painted my body. Now, though, I wonder what it meant for him to look at me as a shape, a subject, and then sleep with me, in the very same room. For a while it was the one place he didn't have boundaries.

After work we'd eat, usually in a little Italian restaurant on Judd Street. I didn't know what I liked. I ordered spaghetti bolognese every single time.

In return for sitting for Patrick he paid my rent. It seemed like a simple arrangement. Neat, even. I didn't question it, not even once. I was grateful. I had no money, no friends. Patrick was all I had.

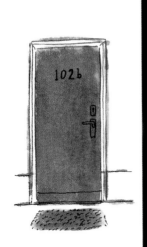

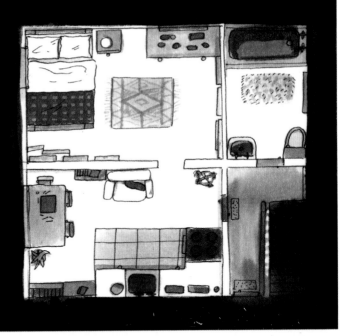

I love this
on of you. X

Dinner at 9?

P. X

Sit for me tomorrow?

14 Finch Lane
Bridport
Dorset

Dearest Alison,
        Thankyou for the note with
your new address. We hope you've
settled in okay. There's some stuff
here for you from the cottage,
you'll have to collect it next
time you're here as it's too expensive
to post.
    I've included my casserole
recipe; it's cheap to make and
very filling. As you know it's
important you look after yourself
up there. Grandma sends her
love.
        Best wishes
            Mum + Dad
                x

Mum + Dad.
All fine here, thanks.
Lots to do. Enclosed
a little drawing. Maybe
it'll be worth something
some day! A xxx

So, next week?

Next week.

I'll need the full day to get the work on the wall. Then I think there'll be some journalists to talk to for an hour or two before the thing opens.

OK.

If you come at eight? You'll catch the end. Then dinner with the others.

Which others?

Well, Marianne, obviously, Roger, Anthony. Maybe Susan Ellis and Si Kalman.

I think I'm nervous about meeting your friends.

You'll do fine. They'll think you're beautiful and fascinating simply because you're not from here. Fresh meat and all that.

Have you got anything to wear?

I don't know. What do I need?

Here; go to town, get something special.

At dinner I met his friends. There were more people than I'd expected and I found it hard to keep track. Most of them were incredibly intimidating; not to mention Pat's age or older. They seemed interested in me and asked a lot of questions. 'Alison, what do you think of … ?', 'Alison, have you ever … ?' Each question prefaced, with pointed warmth and kindness, by my name. 'Alison?' They seemed welcoming but I couldn't help feeling that they were trying to trip me up.

They're not as terrible as they seem.

They don't seem terrible. Just terrifying!

You're Alison, yes?

Yes! I'm sorry, I don't know your name... Patrick told me some, but...

Roger. It was my house in Dorset. When you two met?

OH! At Summer Hill? It's a beautiful house.

The gardens are very lovely.

Aah, so you came over to the house then?

It's OK! Haha! Don't look so worried!

God. I'm so embarrassed.

It's OK! I wasn't scandalised! I think it's a very brave thing you did. Starting again like that, taking a risk.

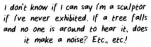

It alarms me to think that had it been left to me, Tessa and I would never have become friends. I was so young and *so sure* that I was the most misplaced person in that room, in every room. I couldn't see that Tessa, who seemed just as bright and sharp as anyone else at the party, was on the outside too. Of course she was. I consider it my greatest good fortune that Tessa invited me for a walk the next day, and coffee two days after that. We careened through the early stages of friendship towards a long-lasting and easy intimacy.

Alison,

Roses are red
Violets are blue.
You snore like
a tank,
Please never
sleep here again.

T xx

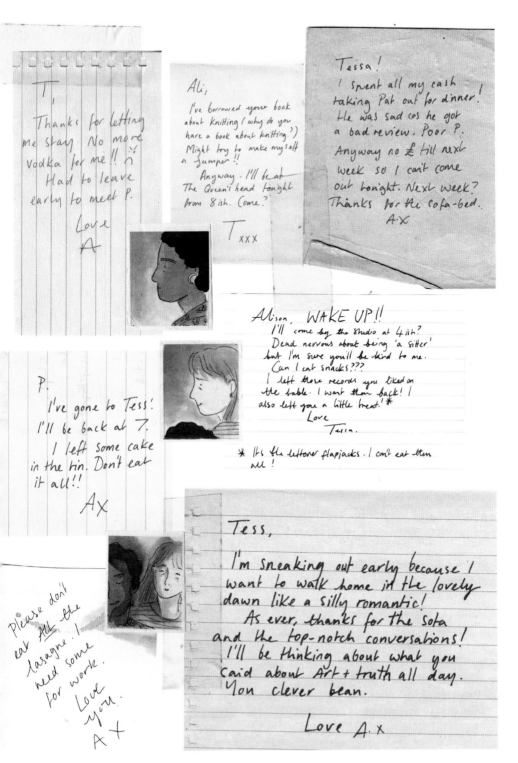

T,

Thanks for letting me stay. No more vodka for me!! 😣 Had to leave early to meet P.

Love
A

Ali,

I've borrowed your book about knitting (why do you have a book about knitting?) Might try to make myself a jumper!!

Anyway. I'll be at The Queen's head tonight from 8ish. Come?

T xxx

Tessa!
I spent all my cash taking Pat out for dinner! He was sad cos he got a bad review. Poor P. Anyway no £ till next week so I can't come out tonight. Next week? Thanks for the sofa-bed.
A·X

Alison, WAKE UP!!
I'll come by the studio at 4ish? Dead nervous about being 'a sitter' but I'm sure you'll be kind to me. Can I eat snacks??? I left those records you liked on the table. I want them back! I also left you a little treat! *
Love
Tessa.

* Its the leftover flapjacks. I can't eat them all!

P.
I've gone to Tess! I'll be back at 7. I left some cake in the tin. Don't eat it all!!
AX

Please don't eat ALL the lasagne! I need some for work.
Love
You.
A X

Tess,

I'm sneaking out early because I want to walk home in the lovely dawn like a silly romantic! As ever, thanks for the sofa and the top-notch conversations! I'll be thinking about what you said about Art + truth all day. You clever bean.

Love A·x

51

52

53

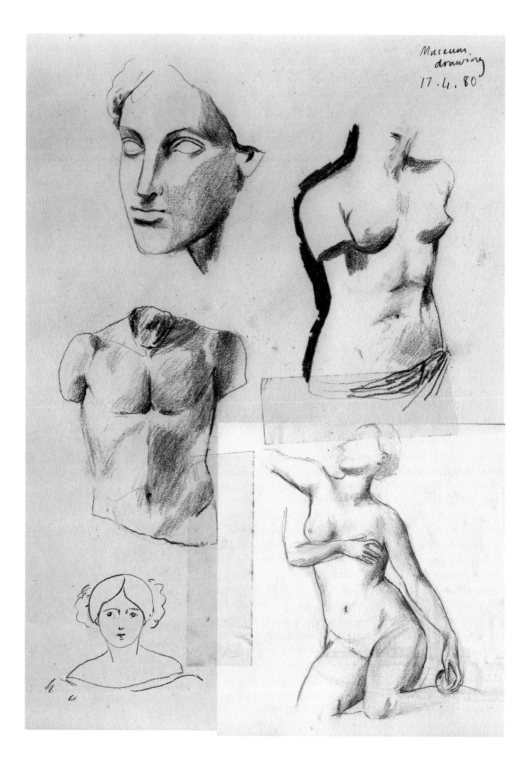

Museum
drawing
17.4.80

54

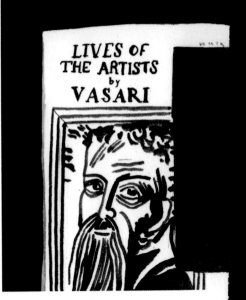

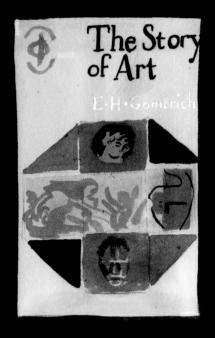

I have a few more that
I'll drop round next week
but these are a good start!
Pat.

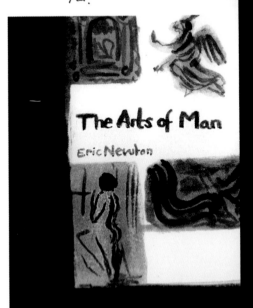

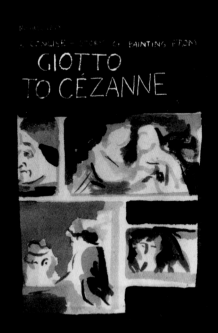

55

You found it! Come in, come in.

This is great. So much space!

It's cold but it's big!

Do I need to do anything?

Nope! Just sit and chat to me! You can move around if you need to.

It's not like a painting. I'm not making a precise image. It'll, I hope, feel like you even if it doesn't look just like you.

I'm excited! I've never been 3D before!!

I'm excited too! I've not done a portrait in ages.

57

We worked so hard, Tessa and I, but for a long time the truth was that we just weren't any good. We were on track to becoming good, eventually, but it would take time. Patrick insisted on drawing practice every day. I spent hours at my drawing board sketching out figures over and over. I had life-drawing classes every week and Tessa and I went sketching at the British Museum whenever we could. I genuinely believed that I was behind and that I should run as hard and fast as I could to catch up.

When I look through my sketchbooks from that time, I struggle to find what in them is mine. Where am I in all these drawings? Even the self-portraits have something of Patrick in them. I filled pages and pages at his instruction but not a single one was my own. I thought that if I could make my drawing perfect, the perfect delicate hand lifted from a Regency portrait or a glistening, watery eye painted in a short series of daubs, if I could get each detail exactly right, then I would be an artist. It was another of Patrick's little misdirects, I think. He told me that getting it right was vitally important because, to him, it was. He and his friends, the writers and academics, had been told their entire lives, 'How clever you are!', 'That's exactly right, you clever boy', 'I think you're the smartest person I've ever met'. Being the cleverest helped them find their place. And so they measured everything by its proximity to correctness. By treating everything with logic, rigour and accuracy they could never be anything less than absolutely right, absolutely the best.

It took me a long time to realise that their approach wasn't going to help me, and that I had to find my own.

Tessa doesn't really draw,
you know. At all.

Tessa is a sculptress.
And a lunatic.

Sculptor.

Sorry?

I said ...
she's a
sculptor.

I know. Anyway, she has no
discipline. It's all chaos with
that woman. One in thirty
of her experiments works,
but barely. You don't want
to work like that.

I love her work. I just love it.

Of course you
do ... You two ...

You're like two little
best friends out on the
playground, aren't you?

You make us sound so silly.

You're not NOT silly.

Dear Mum & Dad

Thank you so much for the gloves you sent at Christmas.
They're perfect. It's not as cold here as it is at home but
when I'm painting my hands do get chilly so they've been very
helpful.

Have you heard from Michael? Do you know where he is now?
I keep meaning to write to him. He sent me a photo when they
were docked in the Bahamas. All right for some, eh?!
    Patrick thinks I've made progress with my painting. He's
taken a few of my small canvases to his gallerist to see if
she knows a gallery who might be interested. I'm sure nothing
will come of it but it's a start!

On Thursdays I've started doing a few hours' work at a
school where I teach drawing to some older pupils. My friend
Tessa used to do the same job but she works in a gallery now
and doesn't have the time. The students are nice, especially
two of the girls, they remind me of Martine and Hilary which
makes me a bit homesick! Anyway I get a little bit of money
and it's another chance to practise my drawing. I feel like
I'm learning alongside them! We even had a model of our own
last week. Not nude! Don't worry, Mum!

Next week Tessa and I are going on a march! Not like when we
petitioned to wear earrings to school but a real one, against
nuclear bombs. Tessa's friends from art school are going too
and she says we'll stay at the back, where it's safer (her mum
insisted, you'll be pleased to hear!).

I'd love if you came to visit at some point. You can stay in my
flat! It's not very warm though. But I'd love to show you London
and you could meet Patrick. I'm sure he'd really like to meet
you. .

Lots of love, A

P.S. Please, if you see him  can you thank Andrew for sending
my things? I did send a note but he hasn't replied. I didn't
expect him to really. Please send my best.

Marianne?

Yes? Have we met?

Uh. Alison Porter? I met you with Patrick ... Kerr.

Ah, Patrick. Yes, of course. You're with Pat.

I wanted to thank you for looking at my work. I really appreciate you found the time even though it wasn't for you.

I've not seen your work, I don't think. Was I meant to? Perhaps you're confused.

Patrick brought it ... to you last week?

He ... Oh. OH. Well. Possibly he hasn't found the opportunity to show it to me yet. We've been very busy.

It's OK, I'm sorry. Thank you. I'm ... sorry for interrupting your day ...

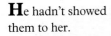He hadn't showed them to her.

Dinner's done!

I didn't say anything. I waited for some sign from Patrick. Some indication that he had kept his word.

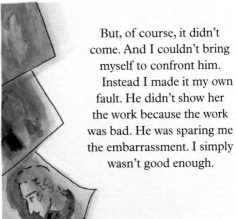
But, of course, it didn't come. And I couldn't bring myself to confront him. Instead I made it my own fault. He didn't show her the work because the work was bad. He was sparing me the embarrassment. I simply wasn't good enough.

Hmm. Where did you find her? Harry?

She was working with Roger. He couldn't get her right so ... passed her on.

Like a parcel.

Sorry?

Passed her like a parcel? Pass the parcel.

You're in a funny mood today, aren't you?

I don't think I am.

Well, either way. I have to go to Cornelissen's. They've got my brushes.

Are we not going to work today?

I've been painting since 7am, darling. I need some fresh air.

So, I'll just go home then?

Go? Stay? It doesn't make a difference to me at all.

The catalogue for that Soutine exhibition I went to in Marseille is on the table, you should take a look. He'd be good for your portraits.

I don't like Soutine.

Well, you should, dear, he's a marvel. But you're clearly in a childish mood so you can leave it if you'd like. I don't want it back filled with crayon scribbles, do I?

Fuck you, Patrick.

Fuck you, too, dear. I'll see you later.

**I** didn't see Patrick for a week after that.
I didn't call him, didn't pop round to make
him onion soup with buttery bread, I didn't
go and sit for him either. Roger called half-
way through the week to tell me that Patrick
had got very drunk the previous night.
Patrick was often, if not constantly, lightly
inebriated, but rarely fully drunk. Roger
suggested it might be worth checking in. 'He
seemed sad,' Roger said. 'He'll have to be sad
for a few more days,' I replied. 'He can cope.'

How strange it was to have a week to
myself! I found that there was so much time
in a day if you gave it all to yourself. I didn't
trust all the time I had. It seemed like a trick,
that my days could be my own. Where was
the catch?

I couldn't really remember the specific
point of my upset, but I remembered the
feeling of being wounded and it was so acute
that I couldn't let it go. There was a kind of
truth to my hurt that at the time I couldn't
quite get at. It seemed to point towards so
many other things, but I couldn't let myself
see them.

1981

They don't know anything about art, not really. They don't know about the real stuff of it! All they actually care about is status!

You don't think that's true, do you?

Of course it's true! Not one of the men in that room gives a flying fuck about how it feels to make work. They only care that theirs will cost more than the man's next to them.

I don't think that's fully true.

Nothing I say is FULLY true! But do y'know what I mean?

Maybe?

You see how they are. And how they don't include us in that? We're not ... really in their game.

I suppose ...

And, well, if you're not in the game, then I'm ...

Who knows why they think I'm here! None of them bother to ask! I don't think they could imagine that we could be artists too, and be good at it!

I don't think I'm good yet.

Did he tell you that? Of course he bloody did. 'A few more years and you'll be ready for the RCA.' I bet that's it.

Pat has been really helpful. I wouldn't be painting at all if it wasn't for him. I wouldn't know any of this.

77

Tessa meant it about the studio. She phoned me three days later with a place she'd found near the Old Kent Road. I said I'd phone her back but I never did; I suppose I thought I should stay near Patrick. I had this feeling that I was meant to be near to him all the time. She never mentioned it again and instead she moved in with a couple of painters she'd studied with.

I knew that Tessa didn't approve of Patrick. Later she would tell me as much. They avoided each other at all costs. During those years, she kept quiet out of kindness. She was always so kind to me.

**P**atrick took me to a garden party. On the tube I referred to it as a barbecue and Patrick rolled his eyes.

'Don't let Frank hear you talk about it like that. He's invited half the bloody House of Lords.'

Am I going to know anyone?

I don't know. Maybe Marianne? Frank?

We're off here.

**P**atrick went to fetch our drinks and left me sitting on a wall. Everything took him twice as long as normal at parties. If I complained that he'd left me alone for too long he'd say, 'You could have spoken to someone. You need to come out of your shell a bit darling. No one is going to do the work for you.' Which was true, I suppose, but it didn't feel like the thing I needed him to say.

Listen, will you two excuse me for a second? I've just spotted Allan ...

You look great, Ali, you look so great.

Thanks, Frank.

Another drink?

I'm all right, thanks.

Don't go anywhere though. Stay here? Promise?

Sure, I'll be right here. Won't move.

He's a bit of a shit, isn't he? Our Pat? A bit of a shit.

Frank ... Please ... Don't.

I mean, we love him and he's a genius, but fuuuck he's awful.

He can be hard work, yes.

You deserve better, Alison. As an artist but also as a woman. If you don't mind me saying.

...Thanks, Frank. But ...I'm OK really. It's OK.

You deserve someone else.

I think we should change the subject.

Sorry. Am I being inappropriate? Jesus, I fuck everything up.

I just think there's plenty we could be talking about. How's the book coming along?

It's fucking shit, Ali. Total horsecrap if I'm honest.

I'm sure you'd know how to fix it, you're so good at making things better ... Ali ... Ali?

We had dinner with Frank a week after the party. And lunch a few days after that. He never mentioned it. Patrick didn't mention it. Lunches and dinners and parties and exhibitions, it never came up. It was for me to keep. So I kept it.

In 1982 Britain went to war in the Falklands and I went to war with Patrick. I still went to sit for him, most mornings. Unfortunately for him, it seemed that his paintings of me were amongst his most popular and most highly priced. So even when we weren't talking I went to him. I sat. I think I felt that the paintings were something greater than we were, that to be part of them was to be involved in something important. I truly felt that we were both making the work. Without me there would be no *Alison Reclines*, *Alison and Aspidistra*, *Alison Sleeps*. I knew he didn't see it that way, I knew that. But I always hoped that he felt I was a more active player, more than one of his students who sat for an hour and climbed into his bed for the night. It is strange to think of how many of my own lies I forced myself to believe. I've always been such a bad liar.

**P**atrick Kerr wanted a woman who did not exist. A woman without conflict or thought, who didn't worry about paying bills or cooking meals. He wanted someone who didn't worry about birth control, someone who never got the flu. He wanted a woman who would never need anything from him, yet also who could be utterly reliant on him. He wanted to mould someone in his own image, but for that image to also remain the perfect image of femininity. When he met me he wanted me because I was young and ready to be devoted; later he wanted me because I knew all his rules, and I adhered to them absolutely. When, finally, he didn't want me at all, it was because I had found my own corner of the world and refused to let it assimilate into his.

You have to get better at cleaning these brushes out, Patrick.

I know how to clean my brushes, Alison. I've been at this a lot longer than you have ... My God.

Do you? This one is completely mangled.

Do you need to be here right now, Alison? I need to work and you're being very ... unsettling.

You told me to come over for dinner?

Well, I don't want to eat till later so you may as well go home again.

Christ, Pat.

I had always worried – all my life, perhaps – that I had no personality. I felt that I had missed some key stage in development where one accrues the necessary information to be charming or passionate or interesting in public. Dropped, as I was, into a world where everyone was filled with what seemed like such richness of experience, such expression, I felt like blank space.

Painting came to me comparatively late. Patrick, for example, had been drawing and painting with a degree of seriousness since he was eight years old, keenly encouraged by his parents. Through my school years I had drawn for lessons, as instructed. I might have swirled patterns down the edge of a page of confused Latin notes, or embellished an essay with drawings in the hope it might distract from my poor research. It didn't cross my mind that I might be good at making pictures. It didn't cross my mind that I might be good at anything because no one was good at anything, no one I knew. Or if they were, there was no opportunity to do anything about it. None of us knew what we were aiming at.

When I started to paint I found that the aspects of a personality did exist. Social deficiencies of indecision, passivity and quietness, the ones that Patrick would sometimes scold me for, found their opposite in paint. Suddenly I could enact the things I had no words for, make decisions without pause. For me, it felt more important to be articulate on the page. These images would outlast me. It mattered less and less to me that I didn't know how to sparkle at a dinner party because, at home, in my room, I was attempting to communicate the truth as I felt it.

I didn't understand art in the way that Patrick did, didn't know the grand histories and traditions or the biographies of the Great Men. I didn't have Tessa's experience of an art school where, she said, the best gift is the space and the time and the other students. What I made was entirely my own. Sometimes it was bad and sometimes it was good. As time went on it became good more often.

When my first, tiny, solo exhibition opened in 1983 I walked home, alone, from Clerkenwell Road to my bedsit in Archway. Behind me a party continued at the flat above the gallery, my friends drinking, giddy and having increasingly circuitous conversations. I walked home, dizzy with pride, a red-wine-stained grin across my face. To have done something alone was confirmation of my own personhood and in it I found joy.

Aged twenty-four, I had been married and divorced. I had had a love affair with a 'giant of his field'. I had lost myself over and over and over. And now it was time to start again.

Dear Michael,

Thank you so much for the cash loan. I WILL pay you back ASAP. Please don't mention this to Mum + Dad. They'll only worry.

The new flat is great, a bit broken in places but I'll fix it up. More soon.

Love A x x

BEGINNERS

NEW WORK
by
Tom Beck
Tessa Effiong
Owen Pomery
Alison Porter

McCloud Gallery,
EC1A, JUNE 83

**W**hen I left Andrew for Patrick I suppose that I thought that I was leaving one permanent situation for another. I hadn't really planned on this part of my life ever taking place.

It would have been, just a few years earlier, utterly beyond the realm of my comprehension to imagine that I might be twenty-something, single, living with my friends and trying to build a career as an artist. Yet here I was, impermanent, drifting, totally free. I began a great restructuring, in which everything in my life hung on my work. Second to my work was my own pleasure. The two strands of my new existence.

97

In moving from the safe harbour of Patrick's care and financial support, I found that, like most of my friends, I had almost no money at all. So I worked at a college as a technician in the art department. I helped to clean cupboards, mix paints, and fire wobbly clay pots. Sometimes I worked as a waitress, sometimes I looked after the children of one of the college tutors. With the money left over after my rent and bills, firstly, I would buy oil paints and canvas. After that was food (mostly tinned) and drinks at the pub. If there was anything left on the last Friday of the month, Tessa and I would go to Chinatown for dinner and then to the cinema. We'd stuff boiled sweets into our coat pockets and pour white wine into a thermos, hidden in my backpack. Our best times were those when we seesawed between childhood and adulthood: wine and sweets, fish and chips on the floor of Tessa's studio, screeching with laughter on the bus after a po-faced gallery opening. It was as though we knew that the world wasn't really designed for us, and the knowing allowed us to turn it into whatever we wanted.

Beyond Tessa and our friends, and my work, the times when I felt most at peace were usually as I walked through London with a list of errands in my pocket. I was happy to learn how the city fitted together, how this borough became that borough, how the river curved its grey way through the centre, and which hills gave you the best view of all of it. I knew which streets felt safe and which made my shoulders go rigid with vigilance. I knew the museums that were the warmest in winter if you couldn't afford your heating bill, and the department stores with the nicest toilets. With every trip my map of London grew and my love for the city grew with it. It made me feel capable, which, I suppose, I'd never really felt before.

The very fact of my own independent life was a revelation and I tried my best to make the absolute most of it. We put on exhibitions, we cooked dinner for each other, we got trains to the coast and camped in leaky tents whilst the British weather battered at the canvas. We drove around Europe in a rattly van that broke down at a Belgian service station. We helped Tessa's cousin stage an awful play in the back of a pub. If it was on offer we went for it.

We had our group. People who, like me, had come to London from small, quiet towns and cramped terraced houses. We were lucky, I don't know if we'd have got there these days – too expensive. We were young and scruffy. We lived in shared houses where second- or third-hand furniture was covered in rugs and throws gathered from market stalls all over London. We battled with landlords for working radiators. We raised our angry voices in Parliament Square. We were our own world; our own clubs and pubs and the few galleries that were willing to show our (very unpolished) work.

London was riddled with divides and it still is, really. Sometimes, because of my association with a very famous artist, I'd get an invite to the kind of exhibition or party that Patrick used to take me to. I'd drag Tessa along with me, both of us hopeful that this time it might be fun but fully aware that it almost never was. It was strange. We were, broadly speaking, the same as the people at the parties. We were artists, we had shows and sold work to galleries but, somehow, they seemed to know that, at our core, we weren't the same. Something about them, their way of speaking perhaps, made us prickly and defensive. We'd turn combative in conversation, riled by their casual dismissal of things we cared about. They thought we should 'lighten up'. We were too spiky and difficult to digest. Our sense of humour too strange. We were the wrong fit for the room and, somehow, we were always to blame.

It was better in our world, so we tried to stay there for as long as possible.

**1983**

**1984**

**1985**

## For the time being.
Paintings by Alison Porter

August 1st–27th 1983
McCloud Gallery, EC1A

Alison Porter
SOLO ENDEAVOUR

Works on paper

February 1st–28th 1987
McCloud Gallery, EC1A

Tessa Effiong & Friend

## EFFI-GONG!

Nigerian-British sculptor Tessa Effiong
last night won top prize at new art award-
'The Reynolds Prize'. The prize was
conceived in order to celebrate the
brightest and boldest voices in British
contemporary Art. The trophy and £2000
cash prize was presented by curator
Andrew Kushner of the Institute of Britis

**1986**

**1987**

**1988**

LIFE WORK
Patrick Kerr

ICA LONDON
February 24th-April 27th 1985

Admission· Free

Painters Patrick Kerr and Robert Crofton and sculpture Raymond Wilson-Bond meet HRH the Queen at the RA last night.

Her Royal Highness met with the great and good of the British Art last night at the Royal Academy as part of their anniversary celebration. Kerr, once considered the 'enfant-terrible' of portraiture bent a deferential knee to the Queen suggesting that, perhaps, the wildness of his youth is long behind him.
See Society, p67, for more.

FIGHT RACISM

Don't Hide
GAY PRIDE

SILENCE=DEATH

BAN THE BOMB

FRED'S CAFE

In 1989 I was thirty-one years old. London had changed so much since I'd arrived there eleven years before. I wondered if I had changed too; my paintings definitely had. They were so much more my own without Patrick standing behind me, guiding my hand. People had even started to buy them, something I never could have imagined. Yet, in spring 1989, I felt I had lost my balance.

It began slowly. I would go to my studio to work, but end up lying on the mattress, staring at the ceiling for so long that it began to move above me, swirling and zooming in and out of focus as if my eyes had come loose in my head. Then I'd drag myself home, the world whirling around me as I lurched towards the tube station.

At home all I had in me was sleep. Bundled up in my bed, I'd focus on every sensation in my fuzzy, rattling body. Each one becoming louder as I scrutinised it instead of trying to sleep. Did my head hurt? Were my legs tired? Were my hands shaking? My world got smaller and smaller. Now I remember that year only through the haze of anxious thought and breathless wooziness that accompanied me everywhere.

Tessa had gone to America on a year-long residency. The work she made on that trip would make her famous. I think that what I was feeling was a loneliness, and loneliness became anxiety, and that became exhaustion. For four years I had been part of Patrick Kerr, and then part of Alison-and-Tessa, with Tess providing all my comfort and support. A tiny pocket of my brain wondered if she went to America to get away from me, though I know, truthfully, that wasn't the case. I wouldn't have blamed her though. I'd shifted my devotion to Patrick onto her, her and my painting. And she was gone. Leaving me with my thoughts and total inability to paint. It was the first time in my life I was completely alone. I had no one I could disappear into or hide behind, and without that I fell apart.

*Patrick made you interesting.*
*You don't know anything of life.*
*Your body will betray you.*
*Your mind is falling apart.*
*You won't be able to paint any more.*

**I** had to go home.

More toast? I need to nip up the shops but I can pop some more under the grill?

I'm OK.

Thank you.

Make sure you're eating properly, love. You're looking a bit thin, there.

I'm fine, Mum. I've just been ... I'm fine.

I'm sure you London folk don't have time for eating right. Too busy rushing around.

It's not really like that, Mum.

You'll have to be patient with your mother, love.

I'm not sure I've got it in me.

I don't understand why she isn't interested in my life.

I think she feels left behind. It's hard. She thought you were happy here, but then you chose something ... different.

... Maybe ...

I've hardly opted to live on the moon, Dad. I've not rejected her.

I know, love. You've just ... moved beyond us, I suppose.

It's a good thing. We're very proud. We might not understand it all. But we're proud.

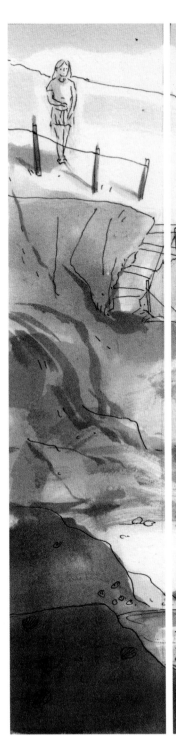

I couldn't make work in Dorset. There wasn't really the space. I'm not sure Mum would have liked my oil paints near her carpets anyway. Instead I walked. I walked up and down the cliffs. I swam in the cold sea, I clambered over rocks and dunes. I think I saw my home for the first time on that trip. I was surprised to discover how beautiful it was.

The rattling in my head began to fade. It would return, of course, from time to time throughout my life, but I grew better at recognising it for what it was: a need to stop and admire the view.

There was one other thing that brought me back to life.

117

Daniel? Daddy says you've been drawing.

Aunty Alison!!

All right Fruitbat!

I've done one of ANGRY and HAPPY.

Oh! I like Angry. It's great.

And this one is Mummy.

And this one is you!

You drew me?

It's got your hair, and your blue coat. And a paintbrush for your artist job.

It's really good.

Now draw me!

**D**aniel was so small. Sometimes, when he cried, he became like one of those tiny baby monkeys, gripping its mother with little bony fingers. I couldn't look right at him, he was like a person without skin. I found being near him – watching him draw, the way he mumbled to himself, the sounds he made whilst he slept against me on the sofa – was the most intoxicating thing I'd ever experienced. He was loveliness embodied, lovely in his bones.

**D**aniel is thirty-four now. He teaches English at a secondary school. He grew out of drawing, like most children do, but the images kept coming to him and now he writes them down instead of drawing them. He sends me great long emails detailing strange scenes he's witnessed in the town where I grew up. When he comes to visit me I take him out for dinner at our favourite Vietnamese restaurant and then we go and watch the silliest-sounding film we can find and drink gin from a hip-flask that I keep especially for these occasions. Daniel is still lovely. For me, he is all joy. We sit in my kitchen, I let him smoke cigarettes indoors as a Bad-Old-Auntie treat, and he tells me all about his life. He calls me Ally-Pally and I call him Danol, which was how he said his name as a child. I never had children. It wasn't a decision I made, I just never had a child. But I had Daniel, and he was all I could ever need.

Alison!
It's for you!

Wait a sec! I'm
coming! I'm coming.

Hello? It's Alison?

Alison?

..................

Alison?

....... Patrick?

Ah, good, you're there.

... I'm here.

I'm sorry to call you. I had to get the number from your gallery.
What an odd lady that curator is!

Sheena? She's very talented.

I'm sure she is. Strange phone manner though.

Patrick, what is it?

Ah, yes. Now. I hate to be the one to
tell you this but Roger died.

Roger? Our Roger?
Roger Blake-Kelly?
Roger died?

Yes. Roger. It seems he was very ill ... Didn't
tell anyone. I suppose we all thought he'd
got bored of us or gone on holiday or
something. But Ivan called me yesterday
and ... He'd been with him at
the hospital at the end.

... Oh, God.

There's a funeral on Friday.
Old St Pancras. Morning, I think.
And a party, of course. I thought
you'd like to know.

Yes, yes. Of
course.
Thanks, Pat.
Are you all right?

Oh, me? Yes, well, you know.
At this age, it begins, I suppose.

Oh, Pat, don't be silly.
You're not that
old. Look, I'll see
you on Thursday,
Patrick. Take care of
yourself.

You too, my darling.

**R**oger Blake-Kelly died as a result of Aids in December 1989. He was forty-eight. We'd had no idea he was sick, of course – that was simply how it went. People were there, smiling across a table over dinner or next to you at the theatre and then, quietly, they stopped coming to parties and exhibitions and then you heard that they'd died, horribly and painfully, sometimes – or in fact often – alone.

I lost four friends to Aids; Patrick and Tessa lost more. That I, at thirty-one, had lost a handful of friends my own age is so shocking to think of now. I know people who lost half of the friends they loved. *Half*. A generation as brilliant as any before or after them, just gone. And Roger, who had been absolutely the kindest person I had ever met.

As well as the fondness we had shared for Roger I think Patrick and I also nursed a tight knot of guilt. That we had not known, that we hadn't been there. We took care of Ivan, Roger's partner, because we loved him but I think, shamefully, we were also trying desperately to appease the feeling that we had failed Roger so terrifically and catastrophically.

Roger's work isn't very well known now, sadly. I have a small canvas painted when he must have known that he was dying. It shows the cliffs near his house in Dorset, painted in the familiar colours of West Country rain. The paint is crusted and thick, layer upon layer of green, grey and blue oil, the impression of his brush-hairs still visible. In the centre of the landscape, at the edge of the cliff, Roger must have placed his thumb in the still-wet paint, pressed and then swiped upwards. The smudge tapers off as he must have reduced the pressure and pulled away; the shape it creates is like the flame on the head of a match. Sometimes I place my own thumb in the indentation, the place where Roger imagined himself, and I long to hear his voice over my shoulder. 'It won't teleport you, dearest!' he'd say, because he could always get right to the heart of the feeling.

I went back to London for the funeral and I stayed. Patrick was taking care of Ivan, at his house in Bloomsbury. I found myself there most nights, cooking dinner and listening to the two men talk about Roger, his endless kindness, his mad, bad paintings, his dark moods and crackling laugh. It felt good to be around them.

I know if Tess had been there, she'd have told me to stay away, but she was still in America. This time was different though.

125

And then it was 1990.

Dearest Alison, ♡

Heartbroken to hear about Roger. He
was such a good egg. I know he meant
a lot to you. I hope you're OK. I wish
I was there to give you a hug.

Ali,
I can't believe it's been †
since I've seen you! Some
record!
The residency is GOOD
of my depth every day
best possible way. I c
FEEL my work getting
single day. I'll be un
the time the year
   The other two a/h†
are so good! Seiko
sculptures that are jus-
beautiful. Alex makes films. He's
very intense. Which...I'm not against!
It's weird spending so much time
with just two people but I'm getting
into it. Making sense at Americans. Slowly!

NEVADA

127

IVANS 48th.
90.

RENOIR
19·00
PRIVATE ROAD
ADULT 2·90         07

RENOIR
16·40
CLEO FROM 5·
ADULT 2·90         04

STUDIO - May 1990

RENOIR
20·30
A WOMAN UNDER -
ADULT 2·90         19

131

Tessa Effiong &
Alison Porter
in conversation
McCloud Gallery

27th August, 7pm

Patrick Kerr died of a heart attack on 17 February 1998.

I was on holiday with a boyfriend, who I knew wouldn't last, in Morocco. I saw the news on the front page of a newspaper. I didn't go back for the funeral, though I thought about it. Instead I spent a week wandering Marrakesh not quite in my own body, not quite in the world.

**P**eople are there and then they're not. Patrick Kerr was my teacher, then my lover, then my enemy, a friend and then, just a memory. I have never stopped expecting to see him when I walk through Bloomsbury. Sometimes I think I do see him, on a book cover in a shop window, a peeling exhibition poster, a man leaning across a table towards a woman who may or may not want him there. Patrick remains everywhere I go. We had a four-year love affair and it has dominated the decades since, but only for me. I don't think Patrick ever got asked, 'What was it like being with Alison Porter?' He has defined my story but I barely made a dent in his.

Patrick Kerr
A Painter's Life
Paintings–1965–97
6 April–30 August 1999

THE TATE GALLERY

How do you grieve a person like that? Someone who pinned you down for so long, yet also was the first to ever offer you a hand? I never quite figured it out and, as a consequence I think, he's never really left me.

Alison,
Here are the paints
I suggested for you.
I think they'll really
enliven your work.
See you tonight.
P. x

How're you feeling?

Sad, tired. A bit ... relieved.

I didn't know he had a bad heart.

Well, you were never his girlfriend!

Will you miss him?

I think ... he'd become a kind of yardstick. I could check back in with him at any point ...

...and find out how I was doing based on how angry or sad or happy he made me feel. I loved his paintings. I loved being painted by him too, for a while.

It's so strange that he's gone.

It is. It's strange how anyone can just be gone.

He was so big. Maybe ... the biggest person I knew.

You know ... he left me his studio?

REALLY? Are you serious?

Not the one in his house, obviously. The attic.

Well ... that's ... nice?!

Isn't it? It's madness really. We'd not spoken for a few years. I think it's probably his way of making himself the centre of my life again. Classic Patrick.

The studio was in an attic on Gower Street. Beneath me students flooded in and out of UCL, on bikes and in Doc Martens, carrying books and pre-packaged sandwiches. I kept the room minimal, as he had. I liked its timelessness. Nothing digital, nothing noisy, an easel, a chair, a mattress and lamps. Patrick had barely used this place, it had mostly been storage for his books and prints. Sometimes he housed his sitters there under the guise of patronage but, most often, as a shortcut to an affair. I had spent the last eighteen years ferrying my possessions from flat to studio to flat. In 1998 I was forty years old and finally, I had a home.

That it was Patrick who was, once again, housing me was typical. I had hoped the studio might have been an apology, for the years we fought through. But I think, simply, Patrick was the kind of person who thought a studio was a good thing to give as a gift. He had never known what space meant to people who didn't have it and, now, this space was mine. It has brought me a peace that has lasted many years.

Tess, opening 2002

Tess,
How many of these
notes have I left
in your kitchen?

Spag-bol is
in the fridge.
Good luck at
the meeting! I
hope they give
you the WHOLE
GALLERY! And
then the whole
city. You
deserve it.

Love, A. X

A!
gold
I think I came up with the last
piece for the show after
our conversation. Thanks
for your good brain.
white?
BRIGHT
blue.
Love
T XXX

143

Do you remember when ...

You know I don't remember anything.

You might remember this! It was ... 19 ... 89?

You can stop there. I definitely won't remember. Your memory scares me! I don't know how you have all this stuff stored up. All those dates. Everything we ever wore or ate.

I don't think I remember the date.

I bet if we gave you a minute or two you'd remember the date!

We were in your Brixton flat. With the cats?

I do remember the cats!

I would hope so. They were your horrible old cats!

So. Brixton. Horrible cats. 1989.

Yes! We were getting ready for your show at ... Krets?

Urgh. That was a really bad show. BAD sculptures. Bad.

See! You do remember things! I knew it.

I remember my own failings, acutely! But the nice stuff? It happens and then it goes away.

That's a shame.

Tessa Effiong was killed in a car accident in 2008. She was fifty-three. I found out four hours after it happened, a call from her niece that left me crumpled and alone in a department store, unsure of how I could get home. Of how I would ever do anything at all without her.

There was a retrospective of her work at the Camden Arts Centre in 2010. The wall-text named her as 'one of Britain's foremost black, female sculptors', which was true. But she was also simply one of Britain's best sculptors, one of the absolute best. Her work made me feel what I felt whenever I saw her, that the world was big and full of potential and that there were things to celebrate, always.

Tessa worked hard her entire life, creating a body of work that was deeply unique. Towards the end of her life she had garnered a good deal of success, with a number of big solo exhibitions. She worked the hardest of all of us. To be a woman and an artist was struggle enough but to ask the patriarchal art world to make space for a Black woman was tougher than I ever could have dealt with. 'They want us to be there but they don't want us to actually be there,' she told me one night in her studio. 'They want all the points for letting us in, for letting me in, but they don't want me to have anything they have.' The structure of the art world was built by men, centuries and centuries ago. We felt that we had been invited into the foyer but we couldn't ever get beyond that. That was their great deception: they made us feel like we were inside when, in fact, inside was an impossibility. Nevertheless, Tessa fought tirelessly, she worked harder than anyone else. Her work was bolder and more beautiful than anyone else's, too. She refused to live in the world they built so she set about building her own. She was my absolute favourite and, perhaps, my truest love.

The whole world should have been looking at Tessa all her life.

# 2019.

I am sixty-one years old. I attend talks at galleries and speak quite regularly at the London art schools I could only have dreamed of attending. I have, over the course of many years, made myself into something new, quite by accident.

Tessa has been gone for eleven years, and Patrick for twenty-one. They left strange-shaped holes in my life, their outlines too specific to ever be filled by anyone else. So I suppose I work around them. The holes. The loss. Tessa's absence is, of course, the most profound, the most difficult to traverse. She is my phantom limb, I feel her all the time and yet I cannot reach out and touch her. I long for her, my best-ever friend.

And yet, it has been eleven years and I have carried on, and found a kind of peace, even with my missing parts.

To hear me speak, low and calm, accentless, you would assume I had the benefit of a London upbringing,

a thorough education. My wool coat is plain but has an air of classic simplicity that, on close inspection, tells you that I have some money. I don't say this to be arrogant. I am simply marvelling at how, without my knowing, I have assimilated myself into the world of the very people I was so intimidated by when I arrived here. It was never my plan. When I walk around Bloomsbury, often I want to tell anyone who'll listen, 'I'm not this person, I grew up outside of all this.' But that feels like a lie. I *am* this person. 'We were always so poor.' I'm like a character at the end of a Dickens novel, having passed through every stratum of society only to end up on top, origins imperceptible to an outside observer.

Sometimes when I paint I feel tired, in a way that, I suppose, must be the slow creep of old age. I wish that Tessa were here to complain to. She'd have been outrageously furious about the whole damn thing.

We're so lucky to be joined tonight by one of Britain's most celebrated female artists: Alison Porter. Alison was born in Dorset in 1958. A self-taught artist, she moved to London in 1978 where she was counted amongst the burgeoning Beginners movement of the mid- to late eighties that also included sculptor Owen Pomery, film-maker Miranda Hamid and Porter's close friend, the sculptor Tessa Effiong. Porter has exhibited nationally and internationally for many years; most recently, a retrospective at the Deakin Gallery has drawn widespread acclaim and attention. Alison Porter is also the winner of numerous prizes including the Beale Prize in 1999 and the Smith-Cusk Painting Prize in 2001. Porter's work in the eighties and nineties focused on portraiture of an intimate yet celebratory nature. Strong colour and lively brushstrokes characterise her work, which has, in recent years, swung towards landscape and abstract painting that recalls the coastlines of her childhood. Please join me in welcoming ... Alison Porter.

Gosh. I'm not sure I recognise my life when you say it all like that!

I'm sure I've missed a fair bit out!

The less glamorous bits! My actual life!

We'll open up to questions from the audience. Please wait for Annabel with our roving mic. Yes, over there.

Firstly, I love your work. It's such a big influence on me. I was wondering, who are the artists you're most enjoying at the moment?

There are so many! I have a sculpture by Tessa Effiong in my bedroom which is the first thing I see every day. It keeps me alive, I think. There's been some nice work on show at the ICA from Kamila Gupta. I enjoyed Lui Minjun at the Hayward last year. I like K. Whittam's photographs, they're very honest-feeling and ... I saw a performance piece by the artist and dancer Kalorkoti last month which, I confess, made me cry so much. There are so many people making great work. I feel as though I can just slip away, no one will notice!

Patrick Kerr was in his late forties when you met. You were just twenty and married. Do you think he crossed a line? Do you think, were he alive, that there'd be Me Too stories about Kerr?

Oof. OK ...

I don't know. Patrick's magic trick was never quite letting you know if he was a monster or a guardian angel. At least for me! Maybe with other people it's more clear cut, and there were definitely many other people. Many, many others.

I wouldn't be an artist if it wasn't for him. He saw something. Whether it was something he wanted to sleep with or something he wanted to educate, I will never know.

It doesn't matter. Either way I became a painter because he made me into one. Or ... I made myself into one on his watch. I can never quite condemn him; he gave me my entire life.

He was a great painter. I loved him, sometimes. I hated him other times. I think that went both ways.

I don't really know what else to say about him. I can't answer your question because ... the answer is the story of my life. I'm not sure if I can face up to re-writing it at this quite late stage.

These days I get an early tube from Brixton, where I live, to my studio, where I paint from 7am to midday. I rest for an hour and a half after my lunch. I always plan on reading.

Then I visit a friend or maybe a museum for the afternoon. Sometimes I teach. I like seeing the students' work, it baffles and excites me. They see the things my generation failed to see.

Sometimes I want to tell them, 'Smash your screens! Paint and paint and paint!' But their world sits on a slightly different axis than mine; it spins differently. It's not fair for me to tell them how to be.

My days pass and I enjoy them. I could never have imagined this is where I'd be. Never. Some days I feel like a relic from another time and I'm not even very old.

It's funny, we're in the history books now. Perhaps not the main ones – gratefully, we weren't terrible or triumphant enough for that. But *British Art History* has a little spot for me and Tessa and Roger, and a little more space for Patrick, of course. We're all there, a few paragraphs and, if you're lucky, an image or two. What isn't there is the story of who we were and how we felt and what time and the city meant to us. I try to find reference to Tessa's wicked, cackling laugh or Roger's incessant Joni Mitchell songs, but how would that get in there? All of that is just for me now and, soon it'll be gone altogether. The work will outlive us, it'll remind people that we were here. I hope they like it. We tried really, really hard.

I have to go, I said I'd help assemble a bookcase.

She can pay someone to do that, surely.

Come on, Pat, not everyone has money to burn.

Unlike you.

The revolution will come for you one day and you'll have to learn to build your own damn bookcase.

I just want to be good at this. And I'm not.

You are! And you'll only get better.

I want to make work that feels like ... finding your place.

Yeah. I get that.

In a hundred years I want a young woman to stand in front of my work and think, 'This is where I belong. This is my home.'

Yeah, you can do that. You WILL do that.

What about you?

Well ... I think ... I want to be better than everyone else! Haha!

Haha! Monster!

It's only half a joke! I want ... all those old men who taught painting, who told me I should paint portraits of myself naked, who held the keys to everything but wouldn't let you even remotely near the gates - I just want them to HAVE to say, 'Yeah. Tessa, she's a great artist. She's the best there is.'

# Alison Porter

# Work Space

7 March – 30 April

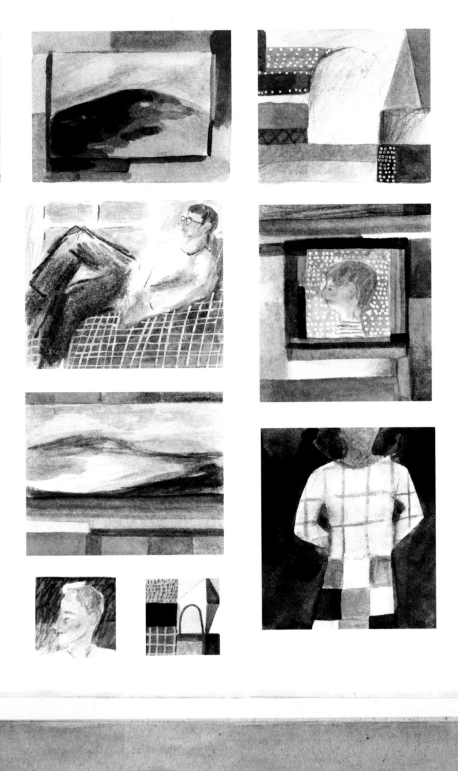

# Acknowledgements

The first draft of this book was written and illustrated during the strange, slow months of lockdown, spring 2020. Whilst the physical experience was incredibly solitary, I wouldn't have had anything to write about without years of conversations with the friends I had come to miss so desperately at that time. Enormous thanks, and lots of love, especially, to Candy Brown, Eleni Kalorkoti and Jennifer Whittam, all three of whom are present in Alison and Tessa.

Thanks to very kind early readers Melanie Hering, Jez Burrows, William Hitchins and Julia Stewart for reassuring me that I had something worth sticking with, and to Kerry Hyndman for swimming round and round a chilly pond with me whilst I waited to see if anyone else was interested in it. To my wonderful agent Jane Finigan for getting on board with this project in such an encouraging and enthusiastic way and for sending Alison into the world with such care.

I am very grateful to Ayoola Solarin for her time and her considered and thoughtful help with the character of Tessa. Thank you to the design and editorial teams at Serpent's Tail for wrangling an odd-shaped manuscript and patiently dealing with the idiosyncrasies of editing an illustrated text. Without their incredible work this would be a far worse-looking book! Thank you to my editor Hannah Westland who has been so open and generous with her support. I couldn't have dreamed of a better home for Alison.

I'm grateful to Avery Hill Publishing: Kat Chapman, Dave White and Ricky Miller; and to Conrad Groth at Fantagraphics for supporting from across the sea. Long-term thanks to Zainab Akhtar, whose kind words, very early in my career, gave me enough confidence to carry on! Also to Steve Walsh, whose 'Small Press' shelves at Gosh! Comics in London were a starting point for so many artists, including myself. On a similar note, meteoric volumes of thanks to Russell Ferguson and Julie Nicol, who encouraged so many artists in Edinburgh in the early to mid-2000s through their shop Analogue Books. I was so lucky to have them on my side when I was still a student. I'm sure they'd deny it, but it really changed the course of my career in a way that I couldn't have anticipated.

I owe a massive debt of gratitude to Barbara Akroyd, who taught my art lessons most of the way through secondary school. Some people are, simply, miraculous, and that I left a Plymouth comprehensive school feeling that art was not only for me but that I could make it myself is almost entirely her doing.

Thank you to Owen Pomery, who spoke with me about these characters every day for many months and who was always so helpful, patient and encouraging, always urging me to continue. Lucky doesn't really begin to cover it.

Finally, my family: the Stewarts, the Meehans, the Taylors and the Kendalls; the lot of them! Particular thanks to the memory of two strange, kind and creative grandmothers: both prominent in my early memories of drawing; they hide between the lines in all of my books. Thanks to my parents, both of whom loaned their handwriting to these pages; a small example of their constant, generous presence in my creative life. I couldn't do anything at all without them, let alone this. And to my sister, Jess, whose handwriting is far too experimental to be in a book but who, nevertheless, is the funniest and smartest person I know. Thank you.